Probability

The Ultimate Beginner's Guide to Permutations & Combinations

by Arthur Taff

Table of Contents

Introduction

The following chapters will discuss, firstly, the essential concepts underlying this entire book: probability, as well as permutations and combinations and how they complement it. We'll be going into detail as to the essential equations which make up these concepts and the most important things to bear in mind as you work with them. You'll learn mental shortcuts, if you will; handy ways to think about these equations which will make them far easier to understand as you go forward.

Then, after discussing those essential concepts and equations, we're going to focus a lot more on practical applicability. In fact, practical application is what's going to make up the vast majority of this book. There's one primary reason for this: I don't know about you, but I think about math and the sciences in a "peculiar" way. I mean, sure, you can *learn* the underlying concepts. But really, what do you actually accomplish by thinking and not DOING.

There may be myriad reasons for why you're looking into this book. You may be looking for help understanding the difficult content of an algebra or statistics class. You may be learning how to use probability and statistics to your advantage for practical reasons such as advancing your career. You may be starting a business and looking to use probability and related statistical analytics in order to increase your performance and make it so that you take a mathematical approach to certain things like sales and marketing (which will certainly give you a leg up over your competitors).

Regardless of your exact intent, I can almost assure you that you're going to find what you're looking for in this book: an easy in-depth explanation of not only probability but also permutations and combinations, as well as how these concepts can be used in different practical applications in your day-to-day life.

What makes this book better than others on the market? The problem with these books is that all too often, they are bad in one of two ways.

The first way is that they cover a ton of content and never really zero in on a specific concept. This is the kind of learning you'd get from a bigger math textbook. This is great if you want a brief summary of a concept or a textbook definition of usage, or a certain formula; but as far as actually understanding the concept or knowing how to use it practically? Good luck.

And as for the other way: there are a lot of books out there that get *too* simple and *too* specific. And these books, much like the others, fail to teach effectively the concepts in question, but for an entirely different reason. These books fail to properly address enough situations so that you can see the multiple ways in which such a broad concept as probability can be used, especially the extremely useful extensions of permutations and combinations.

So, I invite you to put your math fedora on and get ready to learn real-world applications of some of the most useful equations to date! Every effort was made to ensure it is full of as much useful information as possible, please enjoy! I'm certain that you won't regret it.

Chapter 1: What is Probability?

I suppose that this really is a better starting place than any. What is probability? I'm sure the answer is obvious, but it's important for the flow and nature of the book that we establish what exactly probability is.

Probability can be defined as the *measurement of a likelihood to occur*. This is relatively straightforward, right? If you were to flip a coin, there's an equal mathematical probability - that is, an equal chance - that you will get 1) a heads, or 2) a tails.

In this manner, we can see that there are two *outcomes*. *Outcomes* are the end result of a single trial of a given experiment.

An *experiment*, then, is a situation involving probability. When you run an experiment, it will yield a certain *outcome*.

There are several different forms of experiments. They could range from something as simple as spinning a multi-colored spinner or flipping a coin, to something as complex as a lottery system. Because there are several different forms of experiments, there are also a great number of ways in which they could manifest.

They all, however, follow the same basic formula.

This formula will manifest in the following way, one hundred percent of the time:

probability = number of favorable outcomes / number of possible outcomes

So, let's head back to the coin flip. Maybe you want it to land heads. Well, that's one favorable outcome. Now how many possible outcomes are there? Two, of course, because the coin obviously has two sides.

The calculation could then be done thusly:

probability (p) = number of favorable outcomes (1) / number of possible outcomes (2)

$p = 1 / 2$

$p = 0.5$

This shows us, then, that there is a 0.5 probability that we'll get a positive outcome, here being heads.

So, now with the most elementary idea of this book out of the way, let's explore the bigger picture here. There are two massive concepts, tangentially related to probability and, indeed, derivative thereof: the ideas of *permutations* and *combinations.*

These concepts are very similar to one another, actually.

Before we jump into them, though, we need to jump into a simpler concept: a *factorial*. What a factorial is is a way of saying "Hey, I want you to multiply n by itself minus 1, repeating all the way down to zero."

This may sound useless, but you'll quickly see how it plays an important role as I explain permutations and combinations.

Permutations

Let's say that there are six people involved in a contest, and you have to give three of them a prize. Let's say that the prize is the same across all of the three winners: a rubber ducky.

Let's give these people names, to make it easier to work with. Off the top of my head, we have:

Bob

Danny

Anna

Jacob

Karen

Susan

Well, okay. Let's start thinking about how we could hand these out.

The first thing we're going to talk about is *permutations*. What a permutation essentially is is a certain way of ordering a set of values or data or whatever, really. That is to say that a permutation gives you *every* single possible result.

In other words, permutations are a way of sorting data where order matters.

Let's say that we have a gold rubber ducky, a silver rubber ducky, and a bronze rubber ducky, and these are going to be given out to the winners. What we have to do is figure out all possible patterns and correlations of these winners.

So, you may be tempted to do the logical thing and just start working through with something like this:

Well, if we start by handing out the gold to Bob, then we have five other people we can hand out the silver to. So, let's work through those. Bob, gold, Danny, silver, Anna, bronze. Bob, gold, Danny, silver, Jacob, bronze. Bob, gold, Danny, silver, Karen, bronze. (...)

This is perfectly fine, and the logic is fundamentally correct. What we're essentially doing is finding out how many ways this set of data could be ordered, correct? We're looking for every different mutation this same set of data could take.

So how could we find the number of permutations in a far simpler way? Well, we could do this by going ahead and using our factorial.

So, in this, we kind of start out by thinking about how many ways we can actually arrange five people *in general*. We'd start with the first, which could be any of the six people. Then the second, which has to be one of the other five. Then the third, which has to be one of the other four. And so on and so forth. This ends up giving us the factorial:

6 * 5 * 4 * 3 * 2 * 1

You see how factorials are useful now?

Anyhow, by the end of this, we'd have the value 720. There are +20 different ways that we could order them.
720

But we only want how many orders of *3* there would be. These are orders of *six*. So how do we find this?

Well, if we only want *k* people, then we subtract *k*, here represented by 3, from the total number of people *n*, represented here as 6. This gives us 3.

So, we find the total number of permutations we're seeking by the following equation:

n! / (n - k)!

So, in this application, it would be:

6! / (6 - 3)!

Or, in other words:

6! / 3!

So, let's fill in their actual values and get a result.

6! = 720

3! = 6

720 / 6 = 120

permutations?

In other words, there are 120 different combinations of gold, silver, and bronze rubber ducky recipients in our contest.

The typical formula to be used for this sort of thing is as follows:

P(n, k) = n! / (n - k)!

Where, just to reiterate, *n* is the total number of items, and *k* represents the "cutoff" so to speak, or the number of ways that *k* different items from the last are able to be ordered.

Combinations

Okay, so let's change the situation a little bit. Let's say that there is no contest. There are just eight people in a room, and they all want a rubber ducky. You only have 3 rubber duckies to go around, though.

Well, this is fine. We can just solve it like the last problem, right?

Let's see, if we start by handing out a duckie to Bob, then we have five other people we can hand out the next to. So let's work through those. Bob, Danny, Anna. Bob, Danny, Jacob. Bob, Danny, Karen. (...)

But there's a problem here. Let's keep going with that line of logic.

(...) Okay, we're done with Danny as the second person. Now on to Anna. Bob, Anna, Danny.

But wait a second. If you do this, then what is effectively the difference between *Bob, Danny, Anna* and *Bob, Anna, Danny*? Well, the simple answer is that there is *no* difference between the two. This is what is called a "redundancy". That is to say that the two sets of data or two combinations are effectively the same.

Since we aren't differentiating what they're receiving, or what their placement is since there's no contest…and we're just being kind and handing out rubber duckies, there is absolutely no practical difference between handing rubber duckies to Bob, Danny, and Anna and handing them to Bob, Anna, and Danny. The same people are still listed.

So, the idea of combinations is to figure out every possible random combination of individuals that we could give those duckies to. Or, in other words, disregarding any specific order or ranking and just seeing how many different ways we could hypothetically hand these out in. These are essentially permutations, but without the redundancies. There are mathematicians that would absolutely kill me for that explanation, but it's the simplest way to explain it.

Anyway, how do we calculate this simply while also accounting for the redundancies?

Well, the way we do this is to create every number of permutations we can have and then divide by all possible redundancies. How do we find how many redundancies we have?

Simple. The factorial $k!$, here being $3!$, will give us how many redundancies we have.

The normal formula for finding the number of combinations is as follows:

$$C(n, k) = P(n, k) / k!$$

So, in other words, if we wanted to find how many *unique* combinations of 3 people out of 6 we could give the rubber duckies to, we would do it like so.

First, we have to find the permutations. We just did this.

$$C(6, 3) = 120 / 3!$$

So now we just have to filter out the redundancies:

$$C(6,3) = 120 / 6$$

$$C(6,3) = 20$$

So, there are in fact only 20 *unique* combinations of 3 to which rubber duckies could be given.

This outlines the major difference between permutations and combinations. Permutations primarily deal with every possible outcome and order of a given set of data. Combinations shirk order entirely and present to you, instead, how many *unique* sets of data can be found from a given parent set.

So those core lessons form the base for the rest of our book. However, there's one thing that I really need to drive home before we move on to the next part of the book:

With permutations, *order* matters. Take for example phone numbers. Every phone number in America is 10 digits, arranged like so:

(xxx) xxx-xxxx

But it can't just be any combination. The order of the number matters. If I'm trying to order a pizza from a place that has the number (555) 123-4567, but I try to call the number (123) 555-4567, I still don't connect to the pizza place just because the numbers are the same.

With *combinations*, order doesn't matter. However, there can't be any duplicates.

Permutations represent every possible distortion of a set of data. Combinations represent every set of data but get rid of any extraneous or duplicative elements.

Read This FIRST - 100% FREE BONUS

FOR A LIMITED TIME ONLY – Get the best-selling book *"5 Steps to Learn Absolutely Anything in as Little As 3 Days!"* by Edward Mize absolutely FREE!

Readers who have read this bonus book as well have seen huge increases in their abilities to learn new things and apply it to their lives – so it is *highly recommended* to get this bonus book.

Once again, as a big thank-you for downloading this book, I'd like to offer it to you *100% FREE for a LIMITED TIME ONLY!*

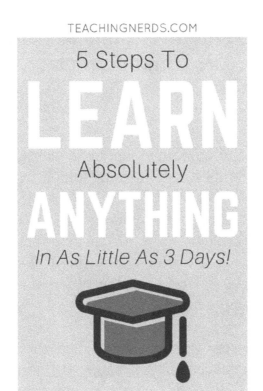

To download your FREE copy, go to:

TeachingNerds.com/Bonus

Chapter 2: Another Angle to Permutations & Combinations

The Basics

Permutations and combinations are a way of determining how many different possibilities of something there are.

Permutations are what you use when the order matters. For instance, if 8 people are racing in a track meet, and you want to find the different ways they could get 1st, 2nd, and 3rd place, then the order matters. So, you would use a permutation.

Combinations are what you use when the order doesn't matter. For instance, if you have 10 different pieces of clothing you want to take on a trip, but you can only fit 7 of them in your suitcase, it matters which 7 you pick, but it doesn't matter what order you put them in the suitcase, so you would use a combination

The Key Mathematical Symbol

There is one key thing to know with Permutations and Combinations, and that is the Factorial. Typically denoted with an exclamation point!

If you want to find how many different ways you can arrange 8 different items, it is 8 Factorial, which is 8 * 7 * 6 * 5 * 4 * 3 * 2 * 1. What this represents is that when you make your first choice of items to arrange, you have 8 to choose from. When you make your second choice, there is one less, so you then have 7 to choose from, then 6 and so on.

Everything with permutations and combinations are just different applications of the Factorial.

Example 1 – Straight Forward Permutation & Combination Problems

Permutations – Slightly Simpler Than Combinations

Let's go back to the track example. Let's say that you have 8 people racing on the track. The total different orders they could come in are 8!

$$8 * 7 * 6 * 5 * 4 * 3 * 2 * 1 = 40320$$

Now let's say you only care about the order of the first three people on the track. Clearly, we would have fewer than the full 8! different permutations, because we only care about how the first 3 people finished, not all 8. So, in that case you have 8 options for first place, 7 options for 2nd place, and 6 options for 3rd place, and that's it.

$$8 * 7 * 6 = 336$$

This is the permutations of 8, choosing 3.

Now there isn't a function that lets us just multiply 8 * 7 * 6 easily. If we wanted the order of everyone, then 8 Factorial lets us multiply 8, down through 1, but it doesn't stop in the middle. The way we do this is by finding 8 Factorial, and then dividing by 5 factorial. We use 5!

because there are 5 items left behind that we don't care about (8-3 = 5) That ends up being

Permutations of Full Set

$$\frac{8*7*6*5*4*3*2*1}{5*4*3*2*1}$$

Permutations of Left Behind Set

The

(5 * 4 * 3 * 2 * 1)

Cancels out of both the numerator and denominator, and we are left with 8 * 7 * 6.

So, to find the permutations of a subset of a group, what we have just done is

- Find the permutations of the entire group (8! in this case)

- Divide by the permutations of the part of the group left behind (5! In this case)

Why are we dividing by the permutations of the parts left behind? Because we don't care what order they are in, so we need to cancel out all different orderings that they can be in.

This is a key point to remember

- If you want to find the permutations of something, use the factorial

- If you want to find the permutations of a subset, find the permutations of the entire group, and then divide by the permutations of the set left behind.

Combinations – Build on Permutations

Combinations simply start as permutations with a subset and add 1 more step.

- Permutations – We take the factorial of the entire set to find the number of possibilities

- Permutations with a subset – We take the factorial of the entire set, and then divide by the factorial of the left behind set

Well for combinations we still don't care about the order of the left behind set, but we also don't care about the order of the set that we have chosen. So, we start with the permutations of the entire set, then divide by the permutations of the left behind set, then divide by the permutations of the chosen set.

So, if we have 10 different items of clothing, and we can only choose 7 to pack, so there are 3 left behind, the number of possibilities are

$$\frac{10*9*8*7*6*5*4*3*2*1}{(3*2*1)*(7*6*5*4*3*2*1)}$$

Permutations of Left Behind   Permutations of Selected Items

Which is equal to 120

An important thing to know is that there will always be at least as many permutations of a set as combinations, and typically many more permutations than combinations.

The Traditional Permutations & Combinations Equations

At this point, it is worth showing the traditional permutations and combinations equations. These are the things that you might typically be expected to memorize for a class, but can be challenging to remember long term

Here is the permutation equation

$$_nP_k = \frac{n!}{(n-k)!}$$

Permutation

Permutation of Full Set

Size of Set

Selected

Permutation of Left Behind Set

And here is the combination equation

22

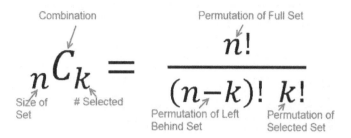

So, while it is manageable to memorize those equations, it is easier to just intuitively understand:

- To find the permutations of a full set, take the factorial

- To find the permutations of a partial set, find the permutations of the full set, then divide by the permutations of the items left behind

- To find the combinations of a partial set, find the permutations of the full set, divide by the permutations of the items left behind, and divide by the permutations of the selected items.

Chapter 3: The Next Step

The examples above were straight forward applications of the combination and permutation equations. However, it turns out that there are a lot of problems where it is not easy to apply those equations directly. If you understand using the factorial, instead of memorizing the equations, you can apply it to cases that the equations don't cover. Take this example, say you have a group of 10 people that are traveling to a destination and you find yourself with 4 vehicles that can take them there. Those 4 vehicles can seat 1 person, 2 people, 3 people, and 4 people respectively, so all 10 people can go.

How many different ways can you organize the groups, assuming that people care about which vehicle they are going in, but they don't care about where they are sitting within a vehicle?

The first thing to recognize is that this seems like a combination problem. The fact that the people don't care where they are sitting means that order does not matter within a particular group. However, the combination equation

$$_nC_k = \frac{n!}{(n-k)!\ k!}$$

is only made for 1 group. If our problem had been that we had 10 people, 4 of which were traveling somewhere and the other 6 were left behind, we could use the combination equation to get the answer. But with the multiple groups this would not work.

So, let's think about what is happening. This is still pretty much a combination problem, but we need to do it slightly differently than the classic combination problem. For every one of these combination or permutation problems we start with the total number of possible permutations that there can be, and then divide out number of possibilities that we do not care about

$$\text{\# of Important Possibilities} = \frac{Total\ Possibilities}{\#\ of\ Unimportant\ Possibilities}$$

To start with, what is the total number of different permutations of the group? It is 10!

That means, if we cared about the order of everyone in the group, we would have 10! Different combinations. But we know we don't care about everyone's order, because we don't care about the order within a specific vehicle, so we know that we will have fewer than 10!

So how many different orders of people do we not care about? To put it a different way, assume that we split the 10 people among the 4 vehicles, so now we know which car everyone will go in. How many different ways could they sit within the vehicles?

- In the largest vehicle, the 4 people could sit 4! different ways

25

- In the next vehicle, the 3 people could sit 3! different ways

- In the next vehicle, the 2 people could sit 2! different ways

- And in the last vehicle, the 1 person could sit 1! different way

So, for any given different groups of people traveling, after you determine what vehicle everyone is traveling in, there are 4! * 3! * 2! * 1! different ways that they can be seated

$$\text{\# of Groups of People} = \frac{\text{\# Total Seating Arrangements}}{\text{\# Seating Arrangments Within The Cars}}$$

We know that the total number of different orders is 10! and the different seating arrangements within the cars are 4!, 3!, 2!, 1!

This means the total different ways the people can be split between vehicles is

$$\text{\# of Groups of People} = \frac{10!}{4! * 3! * 2! * 1!} = 12600$$

Example 3: Mixing Permutations & Combinations

The last problem expanded the combination equation to use multiple groups. This one shows using both combination and permutation equations in a single problem.

26

For this problem let's keep the same 4 vehicles:

- 1 Seat motorcycle

- 2 seat sidecar

- 3 seat golf cart

- 4 seat car

and we still have 10 people that need to go somewhere, however 5 of them are children and 5 of them are adults. Only an adult can be the driver of one of the vehicles.

How many different arrangements are there, assuming that for the passengers it only matters which vehicle they are in, but not where they sit in that vehicle (just like the previous problem) but that it does matter who is driving each vehicle?

To solve this problem, we will need to use both permutations and combinations. We have to split the problem into two parts because there are people who can't be in the driver's seat. So, it isn't applicable to assume that anyone could be anywhere to start with

Total Arrangements = # Driver Arrangements * # Passenger Arrangements

The number of driver arrangements is a straight forward permutation problem. We have 5 people, and 4 seats. We care who is in what seat, and we will have one person left behind where we don't care about their order. The resulting number of driver arrangements is

$$\text{\# of Driver Arrangements} = \frac{5!\ (\text{total adults})}{1!\ (\text{not a driver})}$$

For the passengers, we have 6 possible people, because we have the 5 children plus which ever adult isn't driving. This would mean that there are 6! different arrangements of passengers, however some of those arrangements aren't unique because they are just passengers switching seats within the same vehicle, which we don't care about.

To calculate the total number of unique passenger arrangements we recognize that the 4, 3, 2, & 1 seat vehicles will have 3, 2, 1, & 0 passengers in them respectively. So the

- 4 seat car could have 3! different arrangements of passengers in it

- 3 seat golf cart would have 2! different arrangements

- 2 seat sidecar would have 1! different arrangements

- 1 seat motorcycle would have 0! different arrangements

So, the total number of unique passenger arrangements

$$\text{\# of Passenger Arrangements} = \frac{6\,!}{3!\,*\,2!\,*\,1!\,*\,0\,!}$$

$$\downarrow$$

$$\text{\# of Passenger Arrangements} = \frac{6\,!}{6\,*\,2\,*\,1\,*\,1} = 60$$

When multiplied by the number of driver arrangements

$$\text{Total Arrangements} = \frac{5\,!}{1!}\,*\,\frac{6\,!}{3!\,*\,2!\,*\,1!\,*\,0\,!} = 7200$$

A Side Note on Whole Numbers

One interesting thing to note in all these problems is that we always end up with a whole number. This is because we are asking about real-life events where you can't have a fractional number of different arrangements. For instance, in the last problem you could physically make the people sit in each of the different arrangements and count them (assuming you could get 5 adults and 5 kids to put up with 7200 different seating arrangements) and there would be no way to do only part of an arrangement and have it still be legal.

More mathematically, what is occurring is that the factorials on the numerator and denominator of the permutation or combination equations are always canceling.

For instance, if I had 13 things, and wanted a combination of 7 of them the equation would be

$$\text{Total Combinations} = \frac{13!}{6! * 7!} = 1716$$

The result of 1716 is a whole number, with all of the denominator being completely canceled even though this problem uses the prime numbers of 13 & 7.

The 13! & 7! will cancel out in a very straightforward manner

$$\text{Total Combinations} = \frac{13 * 12 * 11 * 10 * 9 * 8 * 7 * 6 * 5 * 4 * 3 * 2 * 1}{6! * \quad 7 * 6 * 5 * 4 * 3 * 2 * 1}$$

Which leaves you left with

$$\text{Total Combinations} = \frac{13 * 12 * 11 * 10 * 9 * 8}{6 * 5 * 4 * 3 * 2 * 1}$$

And the numbers in the numerator will cancel the denominator out. You could combine them different ways, but the 12 has a 6 factor, the 10 has a 5 factor, the 9 has a 3 factor, and 8 has a 4 & a 2 factor.

As it turns out, this always works and as a result the permutation or combination equations will always give a whole number

Example 4: The Lottery

The Powerball is one of the largest lotteries in the Unites States, and combinations are key to figuring out the odds of winning. This lottery is played as follows

- There are 69 balls in a drum, each with a unique number

- 5 of those balls are selected. The order of those balls do no matter

- There are 26 balls in a separate drum, each with a unique number

- 1 ball is selected from those 26. This is the Powerball. It is possible, but not required, that the Powerball number could match 1 of the other 5 balls chosen because they are selected from different sources.

What are the odds of a single ticket matching all the drawn numbers and winning the lottery?

The solution to this is a simple application of the combination equation.

For the first drum, there are 69 options, chose 5. This means there are:

- 69! total permutations of balls divided by

- 5! which are the permutations of the selected balls, the order of which doesn't matter. The result also divided by

- 64! which is the permutations of the left behind balls, the order of which doesn't matter

So, the total number of possible combinations of balls from the first drum are

$$= \frac{69!}{5! * 64!} = 11{,}238{,}513$$

Additionally, 1 ball is chosen out of 26 from the second drum. The odds of getting all of the balls correct are

$$= \frac{69!}{5! * 64!} * 26 = 292{,}201{,}338$$

So, the odds of winning the jackpot are slightly worse than 1 in 292 million. Each ticket costs \$2, so if you ignored all other factors a lottery with a jackpot of more than 584 million could be a statistically good value.

Interestingly there have been a few Jackpots larger than 584 million. In fact, the largest Jackpot at the time of writing was ~1.6 billion. It is times like those you start to see articles about the profitability of buying every possible ticket. Leaving aside the impossible capital requirements and logistics for an individual or small group to buy 292 million pieces of paper (which, if the tickets are 3 x 5 x .01 inches would be ~25,000 cubic feet, or approximately 30

Uhaul's worth) the claimed profitability of buying all possible numbers ignores

- Shared Jackpots

- Taxes

- Knockdowns for taking a lump sum

To be fair though, I have ignored the lesser prizes that can be won by matching just some of the numbers on the tickets, which improves the odds a little bit.

The final conclusion? The lottery is organized intentionally with odds that make it won every so often in a nation of 300 million people. It is intentionally infrequent enough to yield large payouts, but the odds are small enough that it does get won by someone somewhere at some point. Probably not by you however, and certainly not by me

Just How Big Do Permutations Get?

One interesting thing about permutation problems is that as you increase the samples, the number of possible permutations gets so large, so fast, that it is not possible to analyze all of them. What this book is focused on is how to calculate the number of possible permutations, but what if you instead wanted to list or analyze all of the possibilities?

There are abundant examples where it would be useful to examine every permutation, if that were possible. One classic example is the traveling salesperson problem, which is as follows:

"You have a list of cities you need to visit, and a travel distance between every city pair. Find the route which visits every city exactly one time in the shortest possible distance."

This problem has widespread applications, not just for salesman, but for shipping companies, data routing companies, even machines which drill holes or which test circuit boards. At first glance, it seems the problem seems simple, just make a list of all possible orders of cities and their distances. After all, computers are fast and getting faster all the time. You don't need a fancy algorithm, just analyze everything to find the best solution.

But it is here that the sheer magnitude of permutation problems becomes apparent. Let's say you wanted to calculate the shortest route between 48 points, for instance the 48 state capitals of the lower 48 states in the United States. You have a modern desk top computer, a C++ compiler, and can calculate the total distance of 100 million routes per second.

What happens?

You start your code with a simple data set, only 5 cities. There are 5! = 120 routes that you can take to visit each of those cities one time (although half of those routes are just the reverse direction of a different route) and your computer finds the shortest path of those 120 routes faster than you can measure, certainly less than one second.

Since the code worked for 5 cities, you bump it up to 10 cities. 10! = 3,628,800 different possible routes. So, this calculation still takes less than one second.

At 12 cities however you start to notice a slowdown. 12! = 479,001,600 Since your machine can do 100 million routes per second, this takes approximately 5 seconds, or just enough to notice. 13! Is just over 6 billion, which takes your computer over a minute. By the time you get to 15 cities, it takes over 3 and a half hours to run the analysis on your computer.

Clearly your home computer doesn't have enough processing power, so it is you rent some time on the cloud. Even if you rent 1,000 times the computing power of your personal machine, it still takes almost a day to find the shortest route through 18 cities, and almost a whole year to find the shortest route through 20 cities.

At this point it is time to give up. There isn't anywhere close to enough computing power in the world to go through all the permutations of 48! That is 45 orders of magnitude greater than 18!, which took almost a day to run through on the expensive cloud server.

So, what's the point of this? Simply to demonstrate how big permutations can get. If you have a problem to solve, anything larger than ~12!, it becomes challenging or impossible to iterate through all the permutations, so you would need a more efficient algorithm, or be willing to accept an approximation using a heuristic algorithm.

Example 5: Combinations Applied to Poker

Previously we saw the impracticality of iterating through every permutation of even smallish problems. Fortunately, there are problems of interest that don't require you to evaluate every possible outcome. Simply knowing how many outcomes are possible is useful information. Take for instance Texas Hold'em, which is a variant of poker.

In this game, every player is dealt two cards, which are hidden and for their use alone. Then there are 3 cards dealt in the center of the table that all players share, then another single shared card is dealt in the center of the table, and then a final shared card is dealt to the center of the table, for a total of 5 shared cards over 3 separate rounds.

After you have been dealt your two cards, but before any of the shared cards are dealt, how many different variations of cards can be dealt? For this assume that it doesn't matter what order the three cards are dealt in the first round of community cards (known as the flop), but it does matter which of the 3 rounds the card is dealt in. (round 4 is the turn, round 5 is the river)

To start the problem, you have two cards known to you in your hand. That means that there are 50 cards left to choose from. For the flop, you need to choose 3 cards. This is a combination problem, so the number of possibilities is 50 choose 3. After you have chosen those 3, there are 47 cards left. You pick 1 out of 47 for the turn. Finally, you pick 1 out the remaining 46 for the river. The final equation ends up being

$$= \frac{50!}{3! * 47!} * 47 * 46 = 42{,}375{,}200$$

Starting Deck · Turn · River · Flop · Left behind

So, the total number of different ways the hand could play out is just over 42 million. That calculation might not actually be that useful. A different question is, "You have a starting hand with 2 hearts. What are the odds that you will get a flush by the end of the hand?" This is important because a flush is a powerful hand. You get a flush if there are at least 3 more hearts dealt on the board of the 5 community cards.

Here let's assume that you don't care what order the cards come out in. You only care about if you end up with a flush at the end or not. That means that from your point of view, the total number of possible hands is 50 choose 5, which is different from the result above. The solution of the combination equation of 50 choose 5 is

$$= \frac{50!}{5! * 45!} = 2{,}118{,}760$$

Starting Deck · Community Cards · Left Behind Cards

So, there are 2,118,760 total hands which could be dealt. How many of those give you a flush? To solve this, we need to separately solve for the cases where there are 3 hearts dealt on the board, and 4 hearts dealt on the board, and 5 hearts dealt on the board.

Each suit has 13 cards. You have 2 hearts in your hand, which means there are 11 hearts still in the deck. There are also 39 cards of other suits still in the deck.

- 3 Heart Scenario: There are 3 hearts on the board out of 11 left in the deck. There are 2 non-hearts on the board out of 39. The total number of possible hands is 11 choose 3 * 39 choose 2

- 4 Heart Scenario: There are 4 hearts on the board out of 11 left in the deck. There is 1 non-heart on the board out of 39. The total number of possible hands is 11 choose 4 * 39 choose 1

- 5 Heart Scenario: There are 5 hearts on the board out of 11 left in the deck. There are 0 non-hearts on the board out of 39. The total number of possible hands is 11 choose 5 * 39 choose 0

The equations and results for all of those are

$$\text{3 Hearts} = \frac{11!}{3! * 8!} * \frac{39!}{2! * 37!} = 122{,}265$$

$$\text{4 Hearts} + \frac{11!}{4! * 7!} * \frac{39!}{1! * 38!} = + \ 12{,}870$$

$$\text{5 Hearts} + \frac{11!}{5! * 6!} * \frac{39!}{0! * 39!} = + \qquad 462$$

$$\text{Total Hands} = 136{,}597$$

So, there are 135,597 total hands that could come that would give you a flush. That is out of possible 2,118,760 total hands. That means the odds of getting a flush with two suited starting cards are 135,597 / 2,118,760 = .064 or approximately 6.4 %

Chapter 4: Urn Problem

When you're trying to understand probability, it's super useful to first start with *urn problems*. "What exactly are urn problems?" you may be asking. *Urn problems* are essentially a mental exercise. In this mental exercise, one pretends to imagine certain objects within an urn, which differ by some particular property. The objects in question are usually something like colored balls. The person on the end of the urn problem will pretend that they are removing a ball from the urn.

These can range from very complicated mathematical endeavors to straightforward displays of simple and foundational probability thought.

For right now, let's start with a very simple example of an urn problem. Let's say that there is an urn. In this urn, there are balls of three different colors: pink, purple, and orange. There is also a limitless quantity of balls of each color within the urn. If you were to pull out 7 balls, how many different arrangements of colors might there be in your hand?

The answer to this is really incredibly simple. It also doesn't quite tackle permutation or combination, just yet. The thing that tells us we don't have to use those is that there's actually an unlimited amount of balls. Were there a limited amount, we'd have to use permutation or combination.

All we have to do here to find the number of outcomes is raise the number of options to the power of the number of trials. If we're pulling 7 balls, and there are 3 colors, then we'd just raise three to the power of seven.

3 * 3 * 3 * 3 * 3 * 3 * 3 = 2187
$3^7 = 2187$

Thus, there are 2,187 different arrangements of colored balls that we could have.

Now we'll move on to an example that's a bit more advanced to explain some basic probability in the context of an urn problem. We're going to go ahead and imagine that there are eight balls in an urn: 3 red, and 5 blue.

Let's look at this in really simple terms in order to explain probability.

There are 8 balls total, yes? Let's say that you wanted to pull a red. First let's refer back to that whole probability equation from earlier.

P = number of favorable outcomes / number of total outcomes

There are 3 red balls in the urn, and 8 balls total.

P = 3 / 8

There is thus a .375 probability that you draw a red ball. Now what about blue balls?

We do this similarly. There are 5 blue balls in the urn, and 8 balls total.

P = 5 / 8

There is thus a .625 percent chance that you draw a blue ball.

Now let's do some more advanced arithmetic with this.

Let's say that you were to draw a ball from the urn, and it's blue. How does this modify our probability henceforth?

Well, there's one less ball total in the mix, and one less blue ball. Thus, the fraction for either drops. The probability of drawing a blue ball is now 4 / 7, or about .571, whereas the probability of drawing a red ball is now 3 / 7, or .428. You'll notice that, of course, the chance of drawing a red ball grew higher as the overall proportion of red balls in the urn grew higher.

Let's up the ante a bit. Let's pretend that you put your blue ball back in the urn and we're back to the original proportions. Let's assume, then, that you drew two balls, and the second was a *red* ball. You don't know the color of the other ball, so what is the probability that it, too, is a red ball?

Well, the way that we calculate this is a bit simpler, but all the same, it's still worth going through step-by-step.

If we know that the second ball is a red ball, then we can take that out of the original equation.

3 / 8
-1 / 1

This means that the other ball has a 2/7 chance of being red and a 5/7 chance of being blue.

Another common urn problem which goes a bit more in-depth to the specific theory is as follows: you have an urn, and in this urn are ten blue balls, nine green balls, and eight red balls. If you were to take seven different balls from the urn at random, how often will you draw exactly four blue balls?

This sort of problem generally requires two distinct steps to accomplish. You'll understand this more in the following chapters as it's applied practically. But in the first step, what you're trying to do is calculate the number of all outcomes which may happen. During this step, all you're trying to do is find out the exact parameters of possibility in what you're trying to do. The second step is actually spent trying to figure out the possibility of the *desired outcomes* as a result of the first step, the total outcomes.

So, let's get to solving this. The first step is to determine all of the total *possible* outcomes. This can be determined by doing a simple combination equation.

Since there are twenty-seven balls when you add them all together, this gives us our *n*. The fact that we're drawing 7 gives us our *k*.

Our equation ends up looking as follows:

27! (the number of total balls) / 7! (the number of balls chosen) * 20! (the number of balls left behind)

This yields the following:

27! / 7! * 20! = 888,030

So, there are actually 888,030 different outcomes if we draw at random seven balls from the urn.

So that gives us the number for the first step of solving this. The second step is a little bit more difficult.

What we're trying to do here is determine how many of these outcomes have four blue balls exactly. The way to do this is breaking it into two problems: the first is to look at all of the blue balls and figure out the number of outcomes in which four balls can be chosen. The second is to look at the number of balls that aren't blue and to determine the number outcomes in which three of them are chosen. We then multiply these by each other to get that number.

So, let's break this down. There are 27 balls total, of which 10 are blue. We need to draw four blue balls, which leaves behind six. Our equation ends up looking like this:

10! (total blue balls) / 4! (the number of blue balls which we pick) * 6! (the number of blue balls left behind)

If 10 of them are blue, then there are 17 that are not blue. Of these, we're trying to draw three that are either red or green. This leaves behind fourteen red and green balls.

Our equation will look like this:

17! (the total number of red and green balls) / 3! (the number of balls picked) * 14! (the number of red and green balls left behind)

Then we just have to multiply these off of each other:

(10! / 4! * 6!) * (17! / 3! * 14!)

Which yields 142,800. This tells us that there are actually 142,800 different manners in which we can pull 7 balls and get exactly four blue balls.

Then, we plug this into our probability equation:

P = the number of preferable outcomes / the number of possible outcomes

The number of preferable outcomes is 142,800 and the number of possible outcomes is 888,030. Thus, the chance of us drawing exactly four red balls is:

142,800 / 888,030 = .1608

Which is essentially a 16.1 percent chance. Not too bad.

Example 6: Urn Problems

Urn problems are a classic permutation / combination type of problem. They involve drawing items out of an urn or bag. Those items are distinguished in different ways, often by color. A simple urn problem is:

You have an urn with 3 different colors of balls, red, green, and blue. There is an unlimited quantity of balls of each of the 3 colors. You draw out 5 balls. How many different arrangements of colors can you have? Assume that the order of the balls matters.

The answer to this problem is straight forwards, and doesn't use the permutation or combination equations that we have used before. The key differentiator that informs us not to use those equations was the unlimited quantity of balls. Essentially this is the same as using a random number generator to come up with 1 of 3 numbers for each of the 5 trials.

Since for each of the 5 trials there are 3 possible options, the number of different outcomes is

$$= 3 * 3 * 3 * 3 * 3 = 243$$

Urn problems can be set up to be more complicated. For instance, imagine you have an urn with balls of 3 different colors. In this urn, you have 10 red balls, 9 green balls, and 8 blue balls. If you draw 7 balls randomly from the urn, what percentage of the time will you draw exactly 4 red balls?

These type of problems, where a percentage is being asked, almost always require two distinct steps. In the first step, you have to calculate the total number of possible outcomes. In the second step, you have to calculate the number of outcomes which satisfy the imposed criteria, which in this case is that there are exactly 4 red balls.

46

Dividing the second step by the first step gives a percentage.

Solution: Step 1 Total Outcomes

As always, it is important to determine if the problem needs permutations or combinations. Since in this case it was requested a "total of 4 red balls" and no mention was made on what order they would be drawn in it is clear that combinations are important. So how many possible combinations of balls can be drawn?

There are 27 balls in total, and we are drawing 7 of them. So, this is 27 choose 7

$$= \frac{27!}{7! * (27 - 7)!} = 888{,}030$$

Total Balls: $27!$

Chosen: $7!$

Left Behind: $(27 - 7)!$

There ends up being 888,030 different ways to choose the 7 balls.

Step 2: Desired Outcomes

The second part of this is a little more complicated. How many outcomes have exactly 4 red balls? The trick here is to break this into two smaller sub-problems. The first sub-problem is, of the 10 red balls, how many different ways can 4 balls be chosen. That is the combination formula with 10 choose 4. For the second half of the problem, of the 7 choses balls 3 of them are not red. So, this part is, of the 17 green and blue balls, how many ways can 3 balls be chosen. This is the combination formula with 17 choose 3.

Those two sub-problems are independent of each-other, and for any given outcome on one of the sub-problems, the other one can have its full range of outcomes. That means the two sub-problems need to be multiplied together to get the total number of possible outcomes

The resulting equations are

$$= \underbrace{\frac{10!}{\underbrace{4!}_{\substack{\text{4 Red Balls} \\ \text{Chosen}}} * \underbrace{6!}_{\substack{\text{6 Left} \\ \text{Behind}}}}}_{\substack{\text{Red Balls}}} * \underbrace{\frac{17!}{\underbrace{3!}_{\substack{\text{3} \\ \text{Chosen}}} * \underbrace{14!}_{\substack{\text{14 Left} \\ \text{Behind}}}}}_{\substack{\text{Blue + Green Balls}}} = 142,800$$

So, there are 142,800 different ways that exactly 4 red balls can be chosen when 7 total balls are selected. This means that the odds of getting exactly 4 red balls are $142,800 / 888,030 = .1608$ or approximately 16.1%

Chapter 5: Probability and the Lottery

Alright, so now we're going to get into some more in-depth content and examples by applying the things that we've learned thus far to practical real-life situations.

The first one that we're going to focus on is the lottery, specifically the powerball lottery. We've all heard that whole pipe dream of just buying enough tickets to win the lottery by default, but one really has to ask - is that worth it? And is there any situation where it would ever be worth it?

Moreover, it can be good fun in and of itself to examine the mathematics of winning the lottery to see just how realistic (or unrealistic it is) to spend a lot of money trying to win it.

I think we all know that a person has an extremely small chance of striking it big in the lottery. But when you break it down numerically, it begins to set in just how small of a chance one really has.

When it comes to winning the lottery, the ideas of permutations and combinations are absolutely essential. Combinations more so. In the words of the official Powerball website, you can have any of the 5 drawn white numbers in any order, so long as the numbers match.

So, let's break this whole lottery business down into its core parts and examine how we'd attack this as a mathematical probability.

Firstly, there are sixty-nine balls in every single drum. Each ball has its own number. Five numbers are drawn from this drum - these are the winning numbers. The order of the numbers, again, do not matter.

Next, there are twenty-six balls in another drum. These balls, too, each have their own number. From this number, a singular ball is drawn. This ball is the Powerball. Because they're drawn from different sources, it's *possible* that this ball may match one of the other drawn numbers, though it's unlikely and certainly not necessary.

So, what are the odds that a ticket will be a total match and that the person will win the lottery?

In brief: *very* slim.

But let's break this down mathematically.

Remember earlier how when we had six people and three awards to give, we had to use factorials and then subtract the number of awards from the number of people to get our *k* value? Well, we're basically going to do that again.

So, to start calculating the total probability of matching the first drum, we need to use our combination equation. Let's bring that back up.

$C(n, k) = P(n, k) / !k$

So, let's work out the math for choosing 5 balls from the first drum, given 69 options.

First, we need to establish how many total different permutations of available balls there are. The answer here is 69!. So, then we need to divide that by the permutation of the selected balls. This is 5!. These give us the P(n, k) part of our equation. We'll also have to account for the number of balls left behind, so we need to divide what we've already got additionally by the remaining number of balls - 64!.

Our end equation is something like this:

69! / 5! * 64!

This is, of course, shorthand, and means the same thing as:

(69! / 5!) / 64!

The end result of this equation is 11,238,513. But then we have to add the singular ball from the other drum which is drawn. There are twenty-six options here, so to calculate these odds, we take the answer to our previous equation and multiply it by 26.

11,238,513 * 26 = 292,201,338

What we discover by the end of this is that the odds of somebody winning the lottery are infinitesimally, disappointingly small. In fact, that's 1 in 292,201,338 million. (In theoretical probability, barring any sort of savantism or clairvoyance.)

So, we were pondering earlier whether it would be a good idea to just buy every single ticket possible and go from there? Well, no. Not necessarily. Let's assume that every ticket (in Powerball) costs about two dollars. In order to win the jackpot and have it be worthwhile, the jackpot would have to be well over 900 million dollars in order for you to break even after things such as taxes and reductions for taking the money as a lump sum.

This, of course, isn't taking into account things such as the smaller winnings from various tickets which had correct numbers (just fewer of them), which would also help to make up for the lost money, of course. That's a far more arduous thing to calculate, however, and beyond the scope of this book. Still, calculating that number and adding it to the winnings wouldn't amount to a profit in the end.

So, all in all, the probability of winning the lottery is essentially 1 in 292 million. In other words, you are more likely to be struck by lightning in your lifetime, dye in a plane crash, get hit by a meteorite, write a New York Times Bestseller, or become the United States President than winning the lottery. Individually, not altogether.

The lottery is intentionally designed so that in a country with about three hundred million citizens, it's won infrequently enough so that it pays out very well, but just frequently enough that somebody will eventually win.

Chapter 6: Probability and Poker

If you haven't figured it out, probability, statistics and gambling go hand in hand. All forms of gambling are just games of math, luck if you believe in it, and hopefully not rigged casinos that we all know are actually rigged.

Anyhow, in this chapter, we're going to be looking at how we can practically apply the theories that we've learned thus far to the game of poker.

The first form of poker that we're going to focus on is five-card stud. This is arguably the simplest form of poker out there: you're just dealt five cards and are given the option to replace cards in your hand in order to improve your chances of winning.

So first we have to determine whether we need to use a permutation or a combination for this. Well, in order to determine this, we have to figure out two things. The first is whether or not the order in which the cards are dealt matters. The second is whether or not we can allow for duplicates in our calculation.

The first, whether or not the order matters, is easy. Order doesn't matter. The cards in your hand are the cards in your hand, and you have the same sort of hand regardless of which order your cards are in. 3 number 10 cards followed by 2 number 9 cards and 2 number 9 cards followed by 3 number 10 cards are both a full house. It doesn't matter what order that they're dealt in your hand. So, the first point is moot: order doesn't matter.

The second, whether or not we can allow for duplicates, is also easy. The simple answer is no, we cannot. Duplicates are not at all allowed in this calculation. The reason for this is that we're trying to determine exactly what *different* kind of hands we can get. Because of this, there is essentially no difference between an ace, jack, 5, 7, and 2 hand and a jack, 7, 5, ace, and 2 hand, assuming equivalent suits. They have the same cards, effectively, regardless of which order they're in or which order they were dealt.

Because of this, we're actually going to opt for the *combinations* theorem, not just the *permutations* theorem.

Let's recall the combinations formula:

$$C(n, k) = P(n, k) / k!$$

So, let's think about this for a second. The number of cards in the deck is 52. Because of this n is 52. We're going to be drawing these cards in groups of 5, and so the k is 5.

Let's work this out, then.

$$C(52, 5) = P(52, 5) / 5!$$

So, we need to recall our permutation function:

$$n! / (n - k)!$$

So:

$$52! / (52 - 5)!$$

which becomes:

52! / 47!

This yields the following:

52! / 47! = 311875200

So let's take that and divide it by 5!, per our combinations equation:

311875200 / 5! = x

311875200 / 120 = 2,598,960

So, it turns out that a player can actually be dealt over two and a half million different combinations from a deck of cards just by being given 5 cards from it. That's really crazy!

Now we're going to focus on some cases which are more specific to the variant of poker known as Texas Hold'em. In case you don't know how Texas Hold'em is played: every player in the game is dealt two cards. These cards are kept hidden, and are for their eyes and use only. In the middle of the table are three cards which all players share. Each round, another shared card is dealt, eventually adding up to a grand total of five shared cards altogether over the course of three rounds.

So, we're going to start at a very basic location. You're dealt two cards. Sure, we can work with that. But before even a single one of the community cards are dealt to the center of the table, let's think about how many different sets of cards can actually be *dealt*.

For handling this situation, we're going to establish that it doesn't really matter what order these three cards are dealt in during the first round of shared cards. However, it does matter which *round* the cards are dealt. Round three, for the record, is known as the flop. Round four is known as the turn, and round five is known as the river.

For this problem, we're also going to assume it's a single deck with no duplicate cards. Moving on. To start off, all that we know are the two cards that are in our hand. Since two cards are in our hand there are also fifty cards left on the deck. When the flop round comes, three cards are chosen from the deck.

So, to determine how this could play out, we need to establish this and solve it as a combination problem. Go ahead and pull out your combination equation again:

$$C(n, k) = P(n, k) / k!$$

We're going to go ahead and do this in shorthand again.

So, the first thing that we need to do is take the permutations for the starting deck and the various forms that it could take. Since there are 50 different cards remaining in it, it is thusly a factorial of fifty. We're also only drawing 3 cards, so we need to actually redact those. Our permutation equation would be:

P(50, 3)

Then we have to account for how many cards are left behind, which will give us the unique number of different combinations that we can have with a 50 card deck.

P(50, 3) / 47!

The shorthand for this equation would be:

50! / 3! * 47!

Then we have to add in the next two rounds, where two more cards are drawn. Only one card is drawn each round. Because of this, we can just go ahead and multiply by the number of cards in the deck for each one.

So, we take our initial equation and multiply it for how many cards are left in the deck during the turn round:

(50! / 3! * 47!) * 47

Then we have to take all of that and multiply it by how many cards are left over in the deck during the river round:

(50! / 3! * 47!) * 47 * 46

Then we can draw up our calculation for this, which gives us:

(50! / 3! * 47!) * 47 * 46 = 42, 375,200

So, when it comes to the ways that our hand in Texas Hold'em could play, the answer turns out to be around 42,375,200.

This in and of itself isn't terribly dire information. If anything, it humbles one to how much a game of chance Poker can really end up being. That, of course, is not said to disrespect the Poker greats who know the metagame like the back of their hand and could absolutely wipe the floor with me. But even for them, they can get a bad hand. The difference between a great player and a poor player isn't necessarily in how much luck they have but rather in how much ability they have to play around whatever hand they may end up drawing.

Anyhow, let's go ahead and look at a different situation in Poker. Let's say that in a game for Texas Hold'em, we were dealt two spades. What are the chances that by the end of the round, we have a flush?

Again, in case you don't play Poker, a flush is essentially when you have five cards of the same suit, though not all of sequential rank. This means that you have a flush as long as all five cards are of the same suit, regardless of whether or not they follow each other numerically.

A flush isn't the best hand in the game, but it's certainly not the worst and is a relatively strong hand, all things considered.

So basically, what we're trying to calculate is the likelihood that if you were dealt two spaces, what are the odds that you'd be able to draw a space flush?

Going forward with this, we're going to go with the idea that it doesn't matter what order the cards come in (for simplicity's sake), and the only thing that matters is that we walk out with a flush. So we're doing the combination equation again, but we're going to be doing it in terms of having 50 cards left in the deck and simply drawing 5. This yields a different result from earlier.

To break this down:

We start with the permutations of the starting deck:

50!

Then we divide this by the permutations of community cards that we draw, multiplied by the permutations of the left-behind cards that we draw. This will yield for us the number of possible hands which could result from drawing any 5 cards in the deck.

$$50! / 5! * 45! = 2,118,760$$

So, it turns out that we actually end up with about 2,118,760 different hands that could possibly result from this.

Now that we've got this number, we know exactly how many hands *could* be dealt. But now we've got to figure out how many of these hands would actually result in a flush.

If we want to solve this, we need to do it separately for different circumstances: when there are 3, 4, or 5 spade suited cards that are dealt onto the board.

To do some essential background math really quickly: every suit has thirteen respective cards. Taking this into consideration, we've already got two spades in our hand. From this, we can presume that in the deck are still eleven spades. Naturally, there are thirty nine cards in the deck which are *not* spade suited.

So anyway, let's lay out the various scenarios. We can't just go to this.

If there were to be three spades dealt, then we can assume that there are three spades which are on the board, and two non-spade cards which are out on the board. Thus, there are three out of eleven spades on the board, and two out of thirty-nine non-spades. Because of this, we can draw that the total number of hands that would be necessary for three spades to be on the board.

So how do we write this out in notation?

This will again be shorthand for the combination equation.

So, there are 11 spaces in the deck. We take 3 out, right? Leaving behind 8. So, to find the probability of drawing 3 spades from 11 total, we just have to do the following:

11! (the number of spades) / 3! (the number taken out) * 8! (the number remaining)

Then after that we need to multiply that probability by the number of cards in the deck altogether.

39! (the number of cards in the deck) / 2! (the number of draws remaining) * 37! (the number of cards after drawing)

So now we just multiply these by each other:

(11! / 3! * 8!) * (39! / 2! * 37!) = 122,265

That's how we get the probability of the first draw.

After this we have to do the probability of the second draw. We're going to assume, again, that we have four hearts on the board at this point, which means 7 remaining in the deck. So, let's go ahead and run this formula again, similarly.

11! (the number of spades) / 4! (the number of spades in play) * 7! (the number of spades remaining)

Then we have to multiply that by the number of draws made.

39! (the number of cards in the deck) / 1! (the number of draws remaining) * 38! (the number of cards in the deck after the draw)

So, this equation lends us the following result:

(11! / 4! * 7!) * (39! / 1! * 38!) = 12,870

This gives us the second number for the chances of drawing a flush. Now we just have to do the final one. Again, we're going to modify these equations to fit the appropriate circumstances.

So, the first thing that we're going to do is take a look at the number of spades on the deck. This is assuming there are 5 hearts on the board, with eleven spades on the deck total, which leaves six in the deck.

> 11! (total number of spades) / 5! (number of spades on the board) * 6! (number of spades left in the board)

> So, there's the first half of our equation. Now we have to do this again for the other half of the equation.

> 39! (total number of cards in the deck) / 0! (number of draws remaining) * 39! (number of cards in the deck)

> So, we just multiply these by one another.

> (11! / 5! * 6!) * (39! / 0! * 39!) = 462

> So, then we have the final number 462.

Now we want to get the total number of hands that could come out to give us a flush. So, let's just go ahead and add all the numbers that we've gotten so far.

122,265 + 12,870 + 462 = 135,597

This means that there are 135,597 total hands which could possibly lead to us having a flush.

This is where that number of total possible hands that we came out with earlier comes in handy. That number was 2,118, 760 total possible hands that could be drawn. Now here's what we're going to do.

That's the total number of *possible* outcomes. Now, the total number of spades was our total number of *preferable* outcomes. So, we can determine the probability of drawing a flush from that.

The probability equation is, remember, $P = $ *number of preferable outcomes / number of total outcomes*. So, this resultantly gives us the equation 135,597 / 2,118,760. What does that give us?

135,597 / 2,118,760 = .063998

So, what we discover is that the chances of drawing a flush when you already have two spades in your hand is what comes out to be a 6.3998% chance of drawing a flush during the next three rounds.

You could do these kind of probability equations for any given poker hand. Some fun ones to practice would be the chance of getting a two pair (a hand containing three cards of the same rank and two cards or two different ones, known as "the kickers"), or a full house (a hand which contains 3 cards of one rank and two cards of a different one).

Hypothetical poker situations are actually really great problems to practice probability equations with because it allows you to practice problem solving and gives you a lot of varied hypothetical situations that you could work with. For example, starting with a spade king and queen of hearts, what are the chances that you can end up getting a full house? Mental exercises like these are great for building your strength with these problems, which usually come off as rather esoteric.

Chapter 7: Probability and Weather

We can see probability at work every single day of our lives. We use it constantly, and we even plan around it.

One obvious way that we do this is by forecasting the amount of rain on any given day.

For example, let's look at a sample forecast for a certain day, say February 22nd.

The high could be fifty-three degrees, and the percentage of rain could be 10 percent. If there were a 10% percent chance of rain, this is really just one big probability outcome.

There's of course a lot more to meteorology. But if you were to look at it this way, according to all testing that they've done, they've announced that out of all possible tested outcomes and verifiable empirical observation upon days with similar or identical weather conditions, there's a 45 percent chance that it's going to rain.

That is to say that if the meteorologist who is handling all of our weather forecasts has data for 1000 days wherein the humidity is 68%, the wind is at 8 mph, the sky is partly cloudy, and other very similar atmospheric conditions, he then will start to have a base sample to go off of. This forms the denominator in the precipitory probability fraction. If he can look at this data and determine that on 100 days with conditions like this, it rained, he then can take that data and form a probability equation:

number of favorable outcomes (days which it rained)
___number of possible outcomes (days in total)

Which lends us the equation *100 / 1000*, giving us .10 or 10%.

As I'm sure you've guessed, if we wanted to determine how it would work if we wanted to determine the chance it *wouldn't* rain, they'd go just the opposite way. The number of favorable outcomes, instead of being days where it *did* rain - 100 - would be days where it *didn't* rain, or 900, which would give us 900 / 1000, yielding .9 or 90%, meaning a 90% chance that it doesn't rain.

This just goes to show that probability is truly everywhere, and in most things that we do. It helps to give you a practical way to look at this. There are always a few ways that we could apply this.

Chapter 8: Probability in Horse Racing

This is a seemingly obvious example. Horse racing is a sport as old as the domestication of horses themselves. But permutations fit perfectly alongside this and serve a really simple way to teach a very effective lesson. This too goes alongside gambling (go figure), but offers a really simple jumping off point in order to learn about permutations specifically, and when they'd come in handy.

There are numerous different ways to bet on horse races, but one of the more common is the trifecta. The trifecta is a type of bet in which the horses which you specify must take the first, second, and third place in the exact order that you specified they would. There are various benefits to taking this type of bet, not limited to a big payout. However, it can be a little expensive to play, especially if you have a lot of horses.

So, what are the actual odds of winning a trifecta in bare probability, barring other factors such as a horse's past performance, their current health, the race day conditions, the quality of the horse's care, and so on?

Well let's figure this out. This is perfectly suited to a permutational equation. The first thing that we're going to do is bring back out our permutational equation, just to get a reminder:

$$P(n, k) = n! / (n - k)!$$

So, we want to find the number of different ways that a race could theoretically turn out. First off, we need to know how many horses are entering altogether. Second off, we need to know how many horses we're actually extracting from the results. That is, how many horses we're actually seeing could fit in each permutation. Since we want to know how many combinations of first place, second place, and third place could occur, we're going to have three horses for each permutation.

Let's say hypothetically that our race has 12 horses.

Thus, n is 12. Since we're extracting 3, 3 is k.

Our formula looks thus like so:

$P(12, 3) = 12! / (12 - 3)!$

So, let's do this math here. 12! is basically 12 times 11 times 10 times 9, and so on. This comes out to: 479001600.

Now we have to divide this by (12-3)!, or 9!. 9 factorial comes out to 362880.

So, then we just have to divide the 2:

$479001600 / 362880 = 1320$

There are 1320 *different* permutations, or sets of horses which could place first, second, and third. This means that our statistical chance to win this, only betting once, is 1 / 1320. This comes out to be 0.00075, or a 0.075 percent chance of you winning in a race of 12 horses where all horses are completely new with no prior history, in the same condition, have the same level of care and training, and so on. These variables should make your decision a lot easier, though.

There's also the superfecta. This one is a lot riskier than the trifecta, but you can make a lot of money off of it. A superfecta is when the horses that you name place first, second, third, and fourth in the exact order that you declared. As you can guess, this is extremely difficult to pull off, and you have to be nearly a savant to do it properly. Ah, well, that, or a very experienced better at the horse races. Either way, this is a very high risk/high reward way to make money at the tracks.

So, what are the odds that you actually win the superfecta? Well, since it has to be a specific order, let's go ahead and take a look at this. This will be a lot similar to the last one.

Just for a refresher, we're going to go ahead and pull out our permutational equation again:

$$P(n, k) = n! / (n - k)!$$

So this time, let's assume that there are 20 horses in the race. We're going to be picking four horses in an exact order. This gives us our n, which is 20 (all the horses in the race), and our k, which is 4 (the number of horses that we're picking.)

Let's start by doing our appropriate substitutions:

$$P(20, 4) = 20! / (20 - 4)!$$

Now let's simplify this messiness up a little bit:

$P(20, 4) = 20! / 16!$

Next, let's see what this would be.

20! comes out to be $2.43290201 \times 10^{18}$. In other words, a very, very big number. 16! comes out to be 2.092279×10^{13}.

Now divide the two:

$(2.43290201 \times 10^{18}) / (2.092279 \times 10^{13}) = 116279.99$

This gives us what rounds up to 116280 different permutations of first, second, third, and fourth place in this race.

So, in other words: assuming there are 20 horses racing, and you're trying to do a superfecta, if *every* single externality was accounted for and all of the horses were on equal footing -- I mean, hoofing -- then your chances of winning are 1 in 116280 or 0.00000859 (what is basically .000859 percent).

But hey, at least your odds are better than winning the lottery.

Chapter 9: Binomial Theorem & Pascal's Triangle

One interesting use for the combination equation is to identify outcomes relating the binomial theorem. The binomial theorem deals with the likelihood of discrete events. For instance, if you wanted to answer the question: "If you flipped a coin 10 times, what is the probability that you would get heads 4 times" the way to solve that would be to use the binomial theorem.

The binomial theorem is a topic in its own right, and will only be briefly touched on here. It is mentioned in this book because the binomial theorem incorporates the combination equation into it.

The way to solve the problem of "What is the probability of getting 4 heads in 10 flips" is to

- First calculate how many possible outcomes there could be from flipping a coin 10 times

- Calculate how many of those outcomes result in 4 heads

The number of possible outcomes is simple. There are 2 discrete outcomes for each event, heads or tails. If you choose between those two outcomes 10 times, you end up with 2^10 possible chains of outcomes. 2 raised to the 10th power is 1024

The number of outcomes that will be heads turns out to be the same as 10 choose 4

$$= \frac{10!}{4! * 6!} = 210$$

So, there are 210 possible scenarios to get 4 heads, out of a total of 1024 possibilities. That means that you will get 4 heads   210 / 1024 = .2051   or 20.5% of the time.

Pascal's Triangle

Pascal's triangle is one way of expressing results for the binomial theorem. Every value in the triangle is the sum of the two numbers above it, i.e. the ones with arrows pointing from them in this picture.

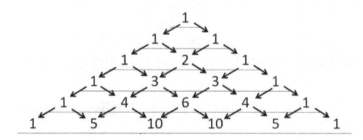

Every row of Pascal's triangle represents 1 more discrete event relative to the row above it. For instance, the top row represents flipping the coin zero times. The only possible outcome from flipping a coin zero times is to get zero heads.

The next row, 1,1 represents flipping a coin 1 time. The first 1 is the outcome of getting zero heads. The second 1 is the outcome from getting 1 head. Note that there are 2 possible outcomes from the 1 flip.

The 4th row with the numbers 1, 3, 3, 1 represents the possible outcomes from flipping a coin 3 times. There are 8 possible permutations of outcomes. In total if you flip the coin 3 times you will get zero heads 1 time, 1 head 3 times, 2 heads 3 times, and 3 heads 1 time.

How this relates to combinations and permutations is that any given value in Pascal's triangle can be calculated using the combination formula. The row number is the number chosen from, and how many from the left a value is, is the number of items chosen. Remember to count both rows and items starting with zero.

As an example, this value of 6 is item number 2 in row number 4

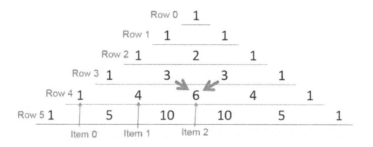

That means it can be calculated using the combination formula of 4 choose 2.

$$= \frac{4!}{2! * 2!} = 6$$

Which in fact it can. The usefulness of using the combination formula to calculate results in the Binomial Theorem is that can save a lot of calculation compared to Pascal's triangle. For instance, if you had to find the odds of getting 50 coins in 100 flips, it is a single equation using the combination equation, but would be 101 rows of numbers using Pascal's triangle.

Example 7: A Programming Permutation Problem

The reason I wrote this book is that I was doing a programming challenge for a large tech company and there were a lot of permutation & combination type programming problems that highlighted the inadequacy of simply relying on the permutation & combination equations. There was a need for a deeper understanding.

This is an example of that kind of programming problem.

Say you have 5 people each with a different height. No two people have the same height. They all stand in a straight line and you stand directly in front of them looking at them.

You can see anyone that is taller than all of the people in front of them, but not anyone that has a taller person standing anywhere in front of them. So, if they stood in ascending height order with the shortest person in front you could see everyone. If the tallest person stood in the front you could only see that one person regardless of the order of the people behind him.

There are 5 people in the line, and you can see 3 of them. How many different arrangements of those 5 people are possible that would have exactly 3 people visible to you?

To begin with, this is a problem that is meant to be solved by writing some computer code. We can and will solve the 5 people with 3 visible manually, but getting too many more people than that would get tedious. Something like 10 people with 6 visible would be fairly hard to do manually due to requiring a fair bit of calculation. (Although that quantity is still within the range of solving in a spreadsheet like Excel with the proper equations set up.

So why do it manually at all? Why not just use the computer program?

The reason is that it is worth understanding how the problem works. Without that understanding you can easily set up your computer code in a naïve way that makes it unable to solve the larger problems either. In fact, if you hit these kinds of problems in a programming challenge you can pretty much guarantee that they have inputs that are large enough that the naïve brute force methods will be unable to solve them, and that you will need to have an understanding of the math to program it correctly.

If you were programming a computer to solve this problem of 5 people with 3 visible, the naïve brute force way would be to just check all 5! = 120 arrangements of people to see if 3 are visible. Checking 120 arrangements would be very tedious to do manually, and certainly you wouldn't want to read a bunch of pages of this book trying to do that, however it would be well within the capability of a computer.

However, permutations grow so quickly that you usually can't try them all for anything but the smallest numbers. For instance, with 10 people, 6 visible there are 10! = ~3.6 million arrangements, which is still solveable on a regular desktop computer but will probably take a measurable second or fraction of one. But solving 20 people 10 visible, there are 20! = ~2.4 * 10^{18} arrangements, which would break any computer in the world to try to look through all the permutations.

Fortunately, we don't need to examine every permutation. We just need to calculate the number that satisfy our criteria for how many people are visible. We can do that more intelligently.

Back to the 5 people with 3 visible problem

The key insight here is that you can't see over the head of the tallest person. So, you can solve this problem by finding where the tallest person is and then how many different arrangements are in front of that person multiplied by the number of arrangements behind them.

So, to start with, where can the tallest person be?

There are 5 people, and 3 visible, so the tallest person must be at least 3 back because if they were any closer to the front, 3 people couldn't be visible.

That means there are 3 spots the tallest person could be in, position 3, 4, or 5

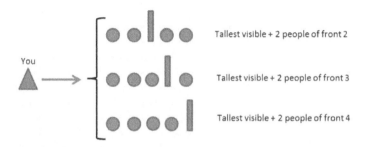

We are going to have to find the total possibilities for each of these cases and add them.

Total Arrangements = # when tallest is at position 3
+ # when tallest is at position 4
+ # when tallest is at position 5

In all of those cases, there are 2 people visible in front of the tallest person, and the only difference is how many other people are in front of the tallest, vs how many people are behind the tallest person.

One way to keep track of this is to make a tree. We want to solve for 5 people, 3 visible, and to do that we need to develop a function that includes 2 people - 2 visible, 3 people – 2 visible, and 4 people – 2 visible

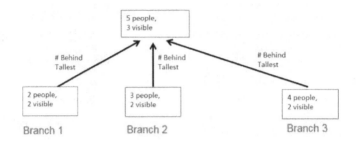

Another way of visualizing the problem, and one that is probably ultimately more useful, is to use a table

# of people					
5			Goal		
4		Branch 3			
3		Branch 2			
2		Branch 1			
1					
# visible	1	2	3	4	5

Solution for Main Branch 1

Let's start with solving for when the tallest person is at position 3. This turns out to be slightly easier than the other two positions as we will see in a minute

At position 3

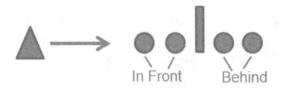

In Front   Behind

Total Arrangements = # Arrangements in Front * # Arrangements Behind

The possibilities behind is a simple permutation problem. Using the classic permutation equation, 4 people, pick 2 (behind)

$$= \frac{4!}{(4-2)!} = 12$$

The number of possibilities for people in front is more complicated. It is not just a classic permutation or combination problem, because we need to take into account the fact that the exact amount of people need to be visible. However here is where this branch of the problem is the easiest. We have 2 people and we know that there have to be 2 people visible. So, there is only 1 possible arrangement for them, the shorter person in the front and the taller person in the back.

That means that there are 12 possible arrangements behind the tallest person, and 1 possible arrangement in front. 12 * 1 = 12, so when the tallest person is in the 3rd position, there are 12 legal arrangements of the other people

● ● | ● ●   = 12 legal arrangements of
　　　　　　　　　　　other 4 people

Let's step back from the problem to fill in some of the table and the tree. This will help us to keep sense of where we are in the problem, although it isn't strictly necessary for a problem of the size of this 5 people, 3 visible.

We just calculated that if there are 2 people, and 2 visible there is only 1 arrangement that works, so we can fill in that square

# of people					
5			Goal		
4		Branch 3			
3		Branch 2			
2		1			
1					
# visible	1	2	3	4	5

In fact, if there are the same number of people as are visible, there is always only 1 possible arrangement, so we can fill in the whole diagonal. Furthermore, there can never be more visible than there are people, so those squares can be grayed out

# of people					
5			Goal		1
4		Branch 3		1	
3		Branch 2	1		
2		1			
1	1				
# visible	1	2	3	4	5

For the tree, we have completed 1 out of the 3 branches

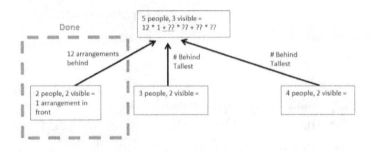

Solution for Main Branch 2

Now let's do the part of the problem where the tallest is in the 4th position.

Once again, the total number of possibilities is the number of arrangements behind the tallest person, multiplied by the number in front of the tallest person.

$$\text{\# of arrangements behind} = \frac{4!\ (people\ remaining)}{3!\ (people\ in\ front)} = 4$$

\# of arrangements in front = Solution with 3 people, 2 visible

However, this 3 people, 2 visible isn't an obvious answer. So, we need to break this down and solve it. Of these 3 people, the tallest can either be in position 2 or position 3. If the tallest was at the front, there couldn't be 2 people visible

Tallest visible + 1 person of front 1

Tallest visible + 1 person of front 2

If the tallest is in position 2, there are 2 solutions because you can switch the people. If the tallest is in position 3, there is 1 solution because of the remaining 2 people, only 1 can be visible.

So, 3 people, 2 visible has a total of 3 solutions. Visually, the updated tree is below.

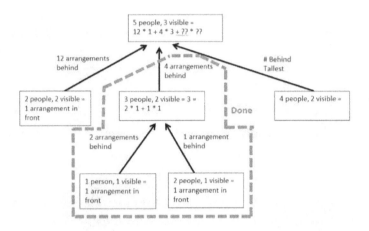

We can also fill out some other parts of the table that we have solved

# of people					
5			Goal		1
4		Branch 3		1	
3		3	1		
2	1	1			
1	1				
# visible	1	2	3	4	5

Solution for Main Branch 3

Now for the last step, we need to find the solution where the tallest person is at position 5.

For this there is only 1 possible arrangement behind, that of 0 people. The permutation equation for this is 4 pick 0, so

$$\text{\# of arrangements behind} = \frac{4! \; (people \; remaining)}{(4-0)! \; (people \; in \; front)} = 1$$

For the number of arrangements in front we have to solve for 4 people, 2 visible. Of these 4 people, there are 3 possible places that the tallest of this group could be. (Side note, you can see by now why this type of problem can get a bit tedious to do manually. Computers are good at this, and there is actually a fairly elegant way to do all of this with the table we have been building in Excel that will be shown at the end)

So, of these 4 people, we need 2 visible. That means the tallest of this group could be at position 2, 3, or 4

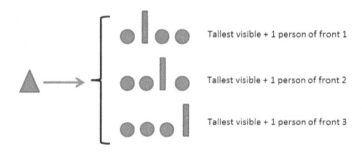

Tallest visible + 1 person of front 1

Tallest visible + 1 person of front 2

Tallest visible + 1 person of front 3

Main Branch 3, Sub Branch 1

If the tallest is in position 2, then

- Behind = 3 pick 2 permutations = $3! \, / \, (3\text{-}2)!$ = 6

- In front is only 1 arrangement of the 1 person

Main Branch 3, Sub Branch 2

83

If the tallest is in position 3 then

- Behind = 3 pick 1 permutations = $3! / (3-1)! = 3$

- In front is only 1 arrangement, since of the two people only the tallest can be visible, so they must be in front.

Main Branch 3, Sub Branch 3

If the tallest is in position 4 then

- Behind = 3 pick 0 permutations = $3! / (3-0)! = 1$

- In front = 2 possibilities. The tallest of the three remaining must be in front since there is only 1 visible, and the other two can be swapped between themselves.

At this point, we have solved all of sub-problems, and the only steps left are to do some multiplication of arrangements in front or behind, and add them all up. **Note, do not be concerned if you lost track of a few of the steps.** This is a tedious problem that is hard to keep track of everything. Doing it as a table turns out to be easier, which we will get to after summing up this solution. What we have is

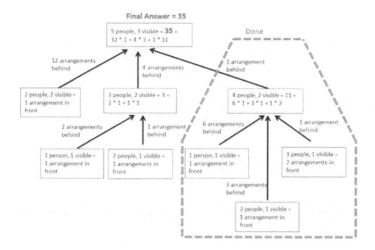

***Our final solution is that there are 35 possible arrangements with 5 people, 3 visible. ***

This are results of the sum of

- 12 arrangements when the tallest is in position 3

- 12 arrangements when the tallest is in position 4

- 11 arrangements when the tallest is in position 5

Drilling down another level, those had sub-sums of

- Tallest in position 3 – Total Sum = 12
  - <u>12 = 12 arrangements behind * 1 arrangement in front</u>

- Tallest in position 4 – Total Sum = 12
  - <u>12 = 4 arrangements behind * 3 arrangements in front</u>

- Tallest in position 5 – Total Sum = 11
  - 11 = 1 arrangements behind * 11 arrangements in front

Drilling down the final level

- Tallest in position 3 – Total Sum = 12
  - 12 = 12 arrangements behind * 1 arrangement in front

- Tallest in position 4 – Total Sum = 12
    - 12 = 4 arrangements behind * 3 arrangements in front
  - 3 arrangements =
    - 2 = 2 arrangements behind * 1 in front
    - 1 = 1 arrangement behind * 1 in front

- Tallest in position 5 – Total Sum = 11
    - 11 = 1 arrangements behind * 11 arrangements in front
  - 11 arrangements =
    - 6 = 6 arrangements behind * 1 in front
    - 3 = 3 arrangements behind * 1 in front
    - 2 = 1 arrangement behind * 2 in front

For the table, what we have calculated is

# of people					
5			35		1
4		11		1	
3	2	3	1		
2	1	1			
1	1				
# visible	1	2	3	4	5

The more elegant table.

We have built up a table for this problem although we haven't filled it in completely. Let's back up a step to where just the diagonals are filled in to see how this problem can be easier to solve using the table.

# of people					
5					1
4				1	
3			1		
2		1			
1	1				
# visible	1	2	3	4	5

The diagonals were fairly intuitive. If you have 5 people, and all 5 must be visible, there is only 1 possible arrangement.

Also, fairly intuitive is the first column. If you have 5 people, and only 1 is visible, that must be the tallest person and they must be in front. So, the other 4 people can be in any order. So, the first column is just the factorial of one less than the number of people

# of people					
5	$4! = 24$				1
4	$3! = 6$			1	
3	$2! = 2$		1		
2	$1! = 1$	1			
1	$0! = 1$				
# visible	1	2	3	4	5

For the other numbers in the other columns, each value is a function of the numbers in the column immediately to the left, and also below it. For instance, 3 people, 2 visible is a function of every cell that has 1 person visible, and 2 or fewer people. In this case that happens to be 2 cells

# of people					
5	24				1
4	6			1	
3	2	3	1		
2	1	1			
1	1				
# visible	1	2	3	4	5

If we were looking at 5 people, 2 visible, that would be a function of 4 cells, because there are 4 cells in the column immediately to the left, that have fewer than 5 people. For 5 people, 3 visible, it would be a function of 3 cells, because there are 3 cells in the column immediately to the left that have fewer than 5 people.

# of people					
5	24	50	35	10	1
4	6	11	6	1	
3	2	3	1		
2	1	1			
1	1				
# visible	1	2	3	4	5

We haven't fully defined the function yet, just identified which cells are contributing. The function is the sum of all the arrangements of people standing in front of the tallest person multiplied by all the arrangements of people standing behind. The values in the cells are the values for the people standing in front, so we need to include the multiplication factor for the number of different ways people standing behind the tallest person can be arranged.

The equation for the how the people behind the tallest person are arranged is fairly intuitive when viewed as this table. It is simply the permutation equation with one less than the number of people in the cell, i.e. everyone except the tallest person as the total number of people, and then picking the number of people behind the tallest person.

Visually it is

# of people		
5	24	50
4	6 * 4p0	11
3	2 * 4p1	3
2	1 * 4p2	1
1	1 * 4p3	
# visible	1	2

In these charts, 4p2 stands for 4 people, selecting 2 using the permutation equation. So, the value of 50 for 5 people 2 visible uses 4 people to select from, because it is one less than 5, and you increase the number of people selected for the permutation by 1 every cell you go down. The full equation is

$$50 = 6*4p0 + 2*4p1 + 1*4p2 + 1*4p3$$

$$50 = \frac{6*4!}{(4-0)!} + \frac{2*4!}{(4-1)!} + \frac{1*4!}{(4-2)!} + \frac{1*4!}{(4-3)!}$$

$$50 = 6*1 + 2*4 + 1*12 + 1*24$$

Another example for a different cell, the solution for 4 people, 3 visible is a function of 3 people 2 visible and 3 people 1 visible. The permutation equation for the number of people behind the tallest person uses 3 for the numerator because 3 is one less than the total number of 4

89

people. The other two cells are then multiplied by 3 pick 0 and 3 pick 1.

# of people			
5	24	50	35
4	6	11	6
3	2	3 * 3p0	1
2	1	1 * 3p1	
1	1		
# visible	1	2	3

$$6 = \frac{3 * 3!}{(3 - 0)!} + \frac{1 * 3!}{(3 - 1)!}$$

Using these equations, it is relatively quick to set up a table for this problem in Excel, here is an 8x8 solution for this problem

# of people								
8	5040	13068	13132	6769	1960	322	28	1
7	720	1764	1624	735	175	21	1	
6	120	274	225	85	15	1		
5	24	50	35	10	1			
4	6	11	6	1				
3	2	3	1					
2	1	1						
1	1							
# visible	1	2	3	4	5	6	7	8

Which was set up using the PERMUT function, for permutations, in Excel

=E9+PERMUT(4,1)*E10+PERMUT(4,2)*E11+PERMUT(4,3)*E12

	D	E	F	G	H	I	J	K	L
4	# of people								
5	8	5040	13068	13132	6769	1960	322	28	1
6	7	720	1764	1624	735	175	21	1	
7	6	120	274	225	85	15	1		
8	5	24	=E9+PERM(	35	10	1			
9	4	6	11	6	1				
10	3	2	3	1					
11	2	1	1						
12	1	1							
13	# visible	1	2	3	4	5	6	7	8

Since this was originally a programming problem, there is also a python program for free at the same location that solves this problem 3 different ways, first using a brute force try every permutation approach, then using the bottom up table like we have shown in Excel, and finally using a top down approach with recursion and memorization.

Conclusion

The next step is to take this knowledge and apply it. See, you can use this knowledge anywhere. And the fact is that probability is pretty much everywhere.

This may not make total sense, but think of it this way: ever heard of Schrodinger? I know it wasn't exactly the point that he was trying to get at, but it was a point made regardless.: things always go one of two ways. Every single thing that ever happens is a choice in one way or another. Maybe not a deliberate choice but a universal choice that nobody else had any idea about. Every single thing has a different way that it could have went.

In this way, knowing these basics of probability is going to help you quite a bit throughout your life when you have to make a difficult decision, or as you try to figure out whether something is truly worthwhile or favorable.

There's quite a lot to be covered on this topic, and realistically we've only scratched the surface. These concepts can go far beyond anything we've covered, and there's even an entire field of mathematics devoted to this sort of thing called—you guessed it—statistics!

Anyway, regardless of what you do with this information, I hope that I've helped you to better understand what's going on "behind the scenes" of all things having to do with statistics and probability. The knowledge base of this course of mathematics is rigorous, difficult, and often incredibly esoteric. It's my most eager hope that somehow I've managed to help you understand these concepts a bit better and maybe possibly even made it a bit enjoyable to learn, too.

Last Chance to Get YOUR Bonus!

FOR A LIMITED TIME ONLY – Get the best-selling book *"5 Steps to Learn Absolutely Anything in as Little As 3 Days!"* by Edward Mize absolutely FREE!

Readers who have read this bonus book as well have seen huge increases in their abilities to learn new things and apply it to their lives – so it is *highly recommended* to get this bonus book.

Once again, as a big thank-you for downloading this book, I'd like to offer it to you *100% FREE for a LIMITED TIME ONLY!*

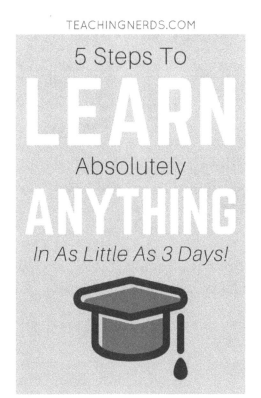

To download your FREE copy, go to:

TeachingNerds.com/Bonus

Final Words

I would like to thank you for downloading my book and I hope I have been able to help you and educate you on something new.

If you have enjoyed this book and would like to share your positive thoughts, could you please take 30 seconds of your time to go back and give me a review on my Amazon book page!

I greatly appreciate seeing these reviews because it helps me share my hard work!

Again, thank you and I wish you all the best!

Disclaimer

This book and related sites provide information in an informative and educational manner only, with information that is general in nature and that is not specific to you, the reader. The contents of this site are intended to assist you and other readers in your education efforts. Consult an expert regarding the applicability of any information provided in our books and sites to you.

Nothing in this book should be construed as personal advice, legal advice, or expert advice, and must not be used in this manner. The information provided is general in nature. This information does not cover all possible uses, actions, precautions, consequences, etc. such as loss of data or hardware failure.

You should consult with an expert before applying anything in this book. This book should not be used in place of learning from a professional or seeking advice from a technical specialist.

No Warranties: The authors and publishers don't guarantee or warrant the quality, accuracy, completeness, timeliness, appropriateness or suitability of the information in this book, or of any product or services referenced by this book, other books, and websites.

The information in this book and on relevant websites is provided on an "as is" basis and the authors and publishers make no representations or warranties of any kind with respect to this information. This site may contain inaccuracies, typographical errors, or other errors.